LET'S HAVE AN ART ATTACK...

WELCOME TO THE ART ATTACK ANNUAL 2004! I HOPE YOU'RE FEELING CREATIVE AS THE FOLLOWING PAGES ARE CRAMMED WITH THINGS TO MAKE AND DO!

WHETHER YOU'RE BY YOURSELF, WITH FRIENDS OR A BROTHER OR SISTER THERE ARE LOADS OF PROJECTS TO GET YOUR TEETH INTO. SO GO ON, TRY THEM YOURSELF!

AND REMEMBER YOU DON'T HAVE TO BE A GREAT ARTIST TO HAVE AN ART ATTACK!

YOU WILL NEED:

old newspapers
cardboard box card
paper fasteners
mixing bowl
colouring pens
pencils
sticky tape
PVA glue
balloons
scissors
kitchen roll
toilet rolls
brushes
paints

£7.50

6
Groovy Guitar

12 String Along

16
Clowning Around

28
Phone Box

30
Veg Out

34 Reward Cards

48
Pinball Wizard

52
All Aboard

66
Art Tower

72
Ark Attack

86
It's a Dog's Life

92
Paint Tidies

 **20** Monster Mouths

22 House of Horror

 **26** Owl's That

 **40** Moving Music

 **46** What a Croc

 **58** Fun Face

 **62** Tin Bin

 **76** Make a Meal

 **82** beggy Laughs

 **102** Crazy Cauldron

 **108** Delightful Lantern

5

AR

YOU WILL NEED:

Cardboard, sticky tape, newspaper, rubber bands, PVA glue, paints, plastic bottle tops, black permanent marker.

Buchanan

TWANG!

1 Cut out two guitar shapes from card and a strip of card about 7cm deep. Tape the long strip of card around one of the guitar shapes, then attach the other guitar shape taping it on firmly.

2 Cut two long pieces of thick card, to make the neck of the guitar. Tape one to the front and one to the back of the guitar.

3 Cut out two pieces of card for the tuning head. On one of the cut outs stick on six cut down straws. Place the other piece of card on top, and tape together.

4 Using newspaper, fill the gaps between the arm of the guitar; make sure you use less newspaper where the guitar arm meets the tuning head. Secure with sticky tape. Attach the tuning head to the end of the arm with sticky tape.

5 Cover with three layers of newspaper and diluted PVA glue. Go in between the straw tuners not over them. Leave it to dry. Make six tuning pegs by using bits of straw with little circles of card stuck on top, cover the top of the tuning pegs in papier maché and leave them to dry.

6 To make the string section, cut out 6 small rectangles of thick card. Divide them into threes and secure with sticky tape. Cut six elastic bands and stick one end of each one to one block and the other end to the other block stretching them taut. Use plenty of sticky tape. Attach this to the front of your guitar.

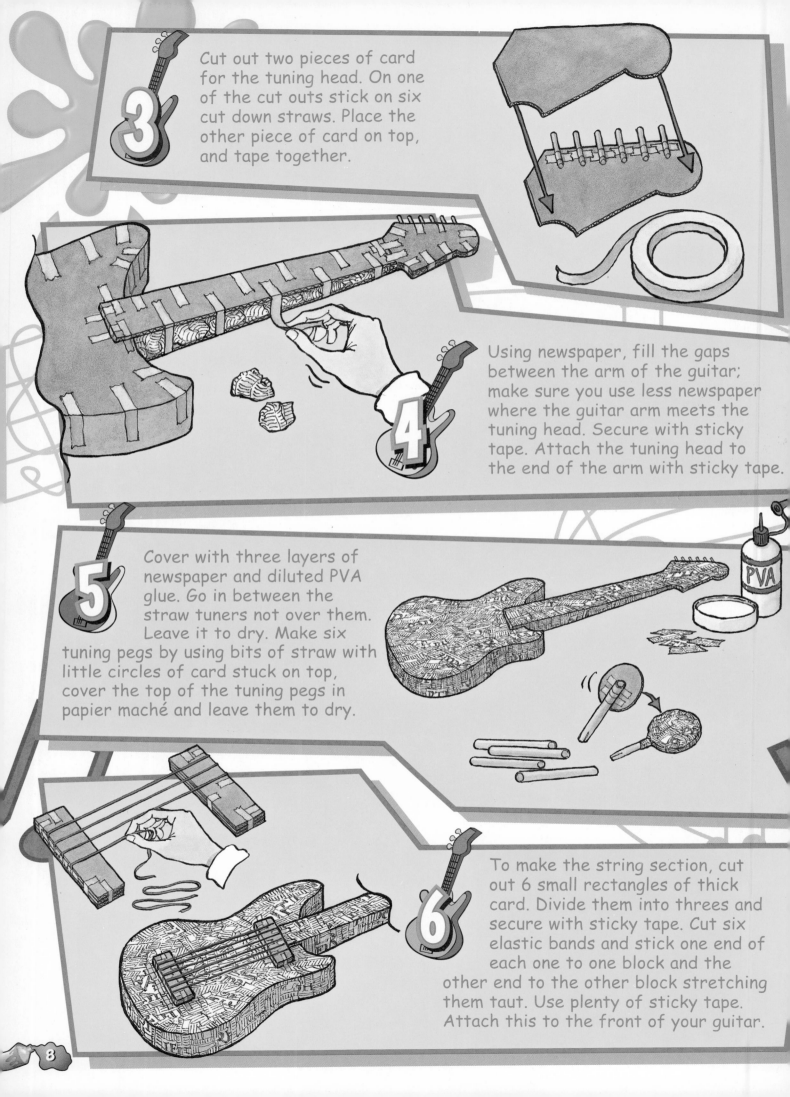

7 Paint the guitar with a funky design. Glue on two bottle tops as buttons. Pinch the straws on the little tuning pegs so that they fit inside the other straws in the tuning head and turn them to tune in your guitar!

USE PLASTIC TOPS FROM A TOOTHPASTE TUBE OR A PLASTIC BOTTLE TOP FROM A DRINKS CONTAINER TO CREATE VOLUME AND TONE KNOBS. STICK THEM ON WITH PVA GLUE.

WHY DON'T YOU FORM A BAND WITH YOUR FRIENDS? YOU COULD CALL IT 'THE ART ATTACKS'!

MAKE SURE THE WIDTH OF YOUR GUITAR IS AT LEAST 5CM. YOU CAN STUFF THE MIDDLE OF THE GUITAR WITH NEWSPAPER TO GIVE IT EXTRA SUPPORT.

WHAT ABOUT ADDING YOUR NAME ON THE TUNING HEAD IN PERMANENT BLACK MARKER?

Buchanan

ELE-FANTA

Elephants are often used during festivals and celebrations in Asia. They are decorated with flowers, ornaments and patterned covers. Have a go at decorating your own elephant, making it as grand and as brightly coloured as you want.

 1 Start by tracing off the elephant on the opposite page. Draw it onto thick white paper or thin card.

 2 Colour the elephant in. Decorate the coverings and chains with felt tips. Use glitter glue, 3 dimensional paints or sequins.

 3 Now carefully cut it out and mount it on a piece of coloured card.

Try making lots of differently decorated elephants and hanging them around your bedroom to make a wall border. Attach each one by sticking the tail of the one in front to the trunk of the one behind.
(Ask an adult before you stick anything to the wall.)

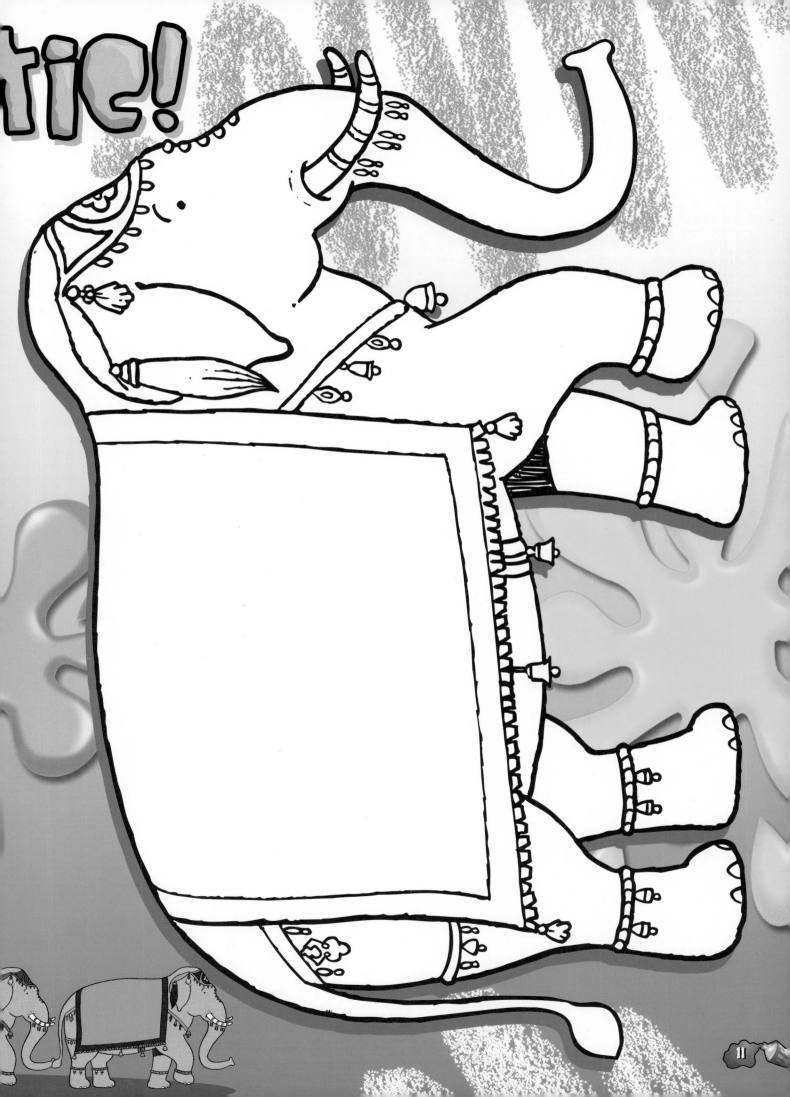

String Along!

GET MOO-VING AND MAKE THIS GREAT STRING HOLDER!

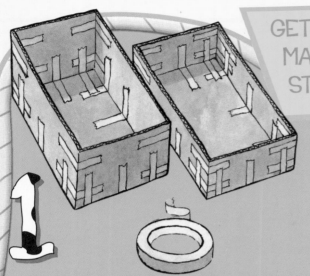

Hole

1

Make the box and lid. (Find a box with a small lid or make a box from cardboard.) You'll need to tape together five pieces of card for each piece. Make the base slightly deeper than the lid.

2

To help it stay on, make a lip to go inside the lid by sticking strips of card around the inside edge. Then join the lid and the base with a strip of paper, to form a hinge. Make a small hole towards one end of the lid for the string to poke through.

Hole

3

To make the cow, glue a length of cardboard tube to the lid. Cut a notch at one end and add a rolled piece of card for the neck. Add another rolled piece of card for the head. Make a hole over the hole you already made in the tail end.

PVA

4

Pad out the shape of the cow by taping on folded strips of kitchen paper and adding ears cut from card. Leave a small space for the string to be pulled through to form his tail.

5

Cover the outside of the box and the cow with four layers of papier maché. Make sure you leave the tail hole uncovered. Leave the whole thing to dry until it is rock hard.

6

Paint the box and the cow using poster paints or acrylics. When the paint is dry, put a ball of string inside the box, pushing one end through the hole.

PVA

TRACE IT!

Trace the pictures on the left onto the right-hand panel and then go over the grey lines. Colour to create your own winter wonderland!

CLOWNING ARO

MAKE A SUPER COMICAL CLOWN MOBILE TO HANG IN YOUR BEDROOM. ALL YOU NEED IS A FEW BITS AND PIECES FROM AROUND THE HOUSE.

1 Roll a piece of card, about 18cm square, into a cone and secure with sticky tape. Trim the bottom edge.

2 Cut two V-shaped slits in the base of the cone, then tape each half, tightly, to form two legs. Stick on a crumpled newspaper ball for a head.

3 Use cardboard tubes or rolled up card for arms. Cut small slits in one end of each tube, then bend back the tabs and attach them to the sides of the cone. (Bend one of them in half to form an elbow.)

4 Add a crumpled paper nose and other features. Cover with three layers of newspaper pasted on with diluted PVA glue and leave it to dry.

YOU WILL NEED!

Scrap card, newspaper, PVA glue, sticky tape, string, balloons, paints

5 Blow up three balloons and cover each one with six layers of papier maché. Stick a loop of string in the top of one of the balloons and papier maché over the ends to secure it on. (You will be able to use this to hang it up later.) Hang the balloons up to dry.

6 Meanwhile, paint the clown with bright colours, poster paints or acrylic paints can be used. When the balloons are dry you can paint them as well.

7 Glue the 3 balloons together, making sure the one with the loop is in the middle. Attach strings to each balloon, and glue or tie the ends to the clown's hands. Finally hang your flying clown up using your string loop.

LOST LIZARD!

CHAMELEONS HAVE THE POWER OF CHANGING COLOUR TO MATCH THEIR SURROUNDINGS, SO YOU CAN HAVE FUN CREATING BOOKMARKS BUT BE CAREFUL YOU DON'T LOSE THEM!

1 Trace the lizard from the bottom of the page to make a template.

2 Place the template on to any sort of paper you like. You could use gift wrap, newspaper, comic pages, old magazines or you can paint it yourself.

3 If you want to use it as a bookmark stick it on to thicker card first. You will then have a plain side to use as a bookmark other wise you will lose your place!

4 Finally, carefully cut the chameleon out and play a bit of hide and seek!

MONSTER MOUTHS!

Colour your three monster mouths in first.

Pull out the whole page and stick it to a piece of thin card or thick paper.

Carefully cut along the red dotted lines and then fold where marked.

FUN?! THEY LOOK A BIT SCARY TO ME!

ART ATTACK

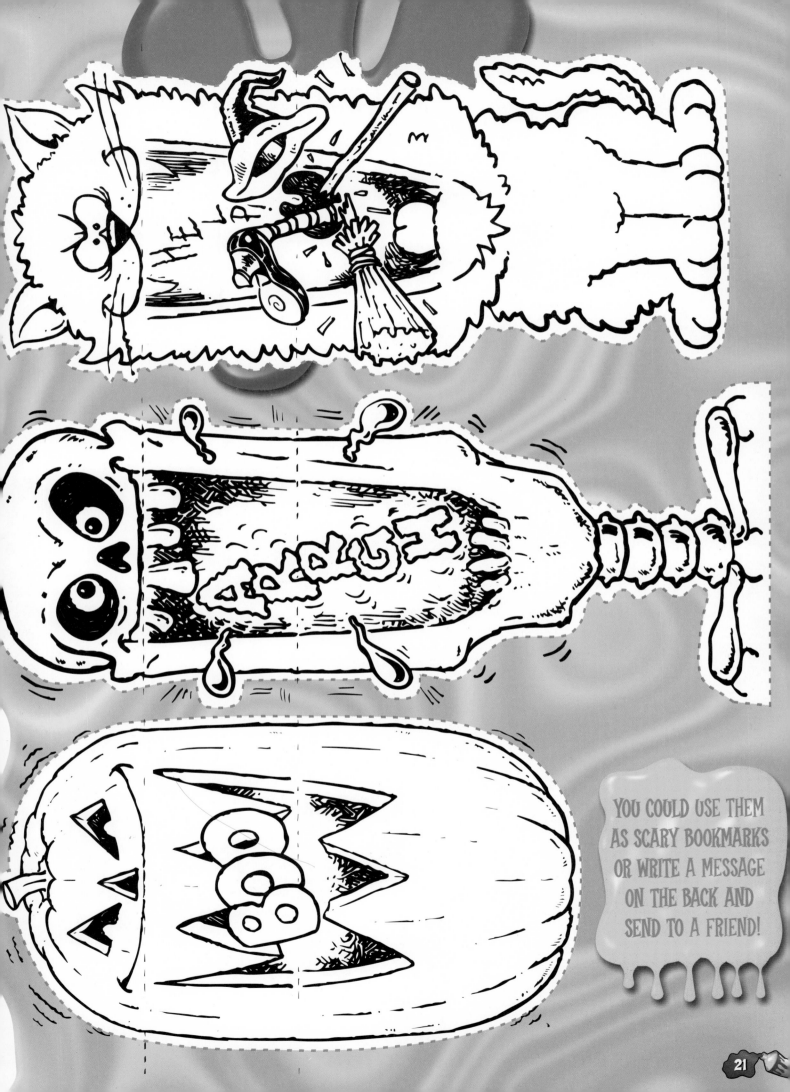

YOU COULD USE THEM AS SCARY BOOKMARKS OR WRITE A MESSAGE ON THE BACK AND SEND TO A FRIEND!

HOUSE OF HORRORS!

WELCOME TO MY HOUSE OF HORROR!
USE YOUR IMAGINATION TO MAKE IT REALLY SPOOKY
BUT DON'T GIVE YOURSELF NIGHTMARES......

1 Stick some cardboard boxes together, using plenty of sticky tape. Start with a big box for the base, followed by a smaller one on the top. Make a roof by folding a square of card in half and attaching with sticky tape.

2 Stick the whole thing on to a large piece of cardboard box card, to make a garden. Add another cardboard box and some tubes to the top, to form towers. Roll up squares of cardboard to make the tower roofs.

TEAR UP A SPONGE AND GLUE THE PIECES ALONG THE EDGE OF THE GARDEN TO MAKE A HEDGE. PAINT IT GREEN. ADD SOME GHOSTLY FIGURES IN THE TURRETS USING BITS OF WHITE FABRIC. FINALLY ADD SOME SINISTER SIGNS.

YOU WILL NEED:

Cardboard boxes, sponge, cardboard tubes, sticky tape, scrap card, plastic bottle top, newspaper, straws, dead matchsticks, paints, PVA glue

3 Add details! For front steps, stick on rectangles of thick cardboard. To make a front door, stick drinking straws trimmed to size onto the wall, above the steps. Add triangles of card to the sides of roofs.

4 For railings, make holes all around the edge of the flat top roof, with a pencil and stick a used match in each hole. Add a blob of glue to each one to hold it in place. Glue on more dead matchsticks horizontally. Add more matchsticks in the garden for sign posts.

SPOOKY TOWERS

5 For the round window, stick on a plastic bottle top. If you fasten it on at one side only, using a piece of sticky tape to form a hinge, the window can be opened and closed!

23

6 When you're happy with the structure, cover the whole thing with four layers of papier maché. Scrunch up bits of kitchen paper and soak them in diluted PVA glue, then stick them around the base of the house, to make bushes. (You could use bits of sponge.)

7 When your model is dry and rock hard, you can paint it! Paint the railings a reddish brown colour to look like rusty metal. Paint the walls grey, with yellow squares for the windows to make it look like the lights are on inside the house. And paint the bushes and grass different shades of green. Add details with a black marker pen.

GHASTLY GHOULS!

Make some spooks to haunt your house of horror!

1 Get an old white handkerchief or a square of old fabric.

2 Place a ball of paper or cottonwool in the middle.

3 Tie some thread around the ball to make a head and knot it tightly. Leave enough thread if you want to hang it up.

4 Finally draw a spooky face!

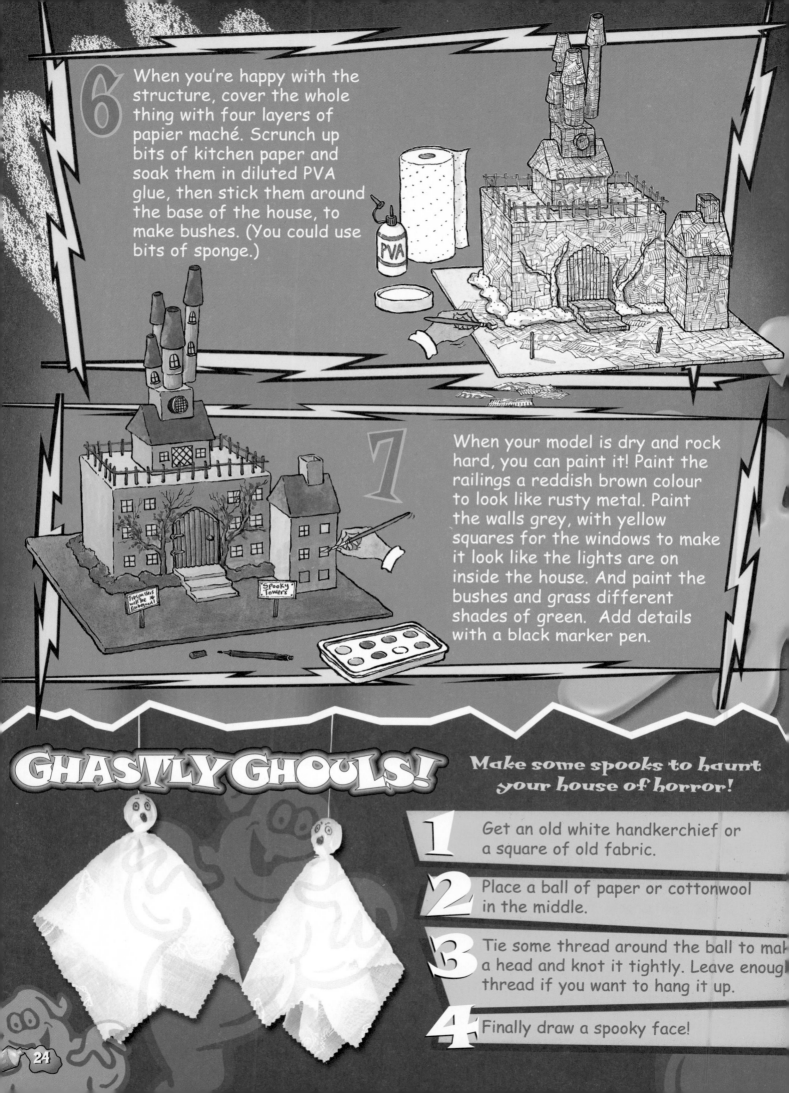

OWL'S THAT?

You can have a real hoot making this brilliant Art Attack! Hang it up in your bedroom and you have a great pet!

1 Blow up a long balloon half way. Tie the bit that is not inflated around the middle of a long cardboard tube.

2 Cut two rectangles of thick cardboard and tape them to the base of the balloon. Cut two long thin rectangles and stick them to the top to form the tail.

3 Tape two crumpled balls of newspaper on for the head and two rolled up bits of paper for the wings. Attach two triangles of card to the head for the ears.

Balloon, cardboard tubes straws, scrap card, string newspaper, sticky tape, paints, PVA glue.

4 For the feet, cut the bendy bits from straws and glue or tape them in place on the cardboard tube.

5 Cover the whole thing with four layers of papier maché. Add a couple of extra layers over the balloon body for extra strength.

6 Leave him to dry and then paint. Finally thread some string through the cardboard tube and hang him up.

PVA

IF YOUR OWL SWINGS FORWARD, ATTACH A STONE OR BLOB OF STICKY TACK TO THE BACK OF HIS TAIL!

PHONE BOX!

1 If you cannot find a small cardboard box with a lid, you can make your own, any size you like! Cut two identical rectangles, for the lid and the base, then cut strips for the sides - about 1cm wide.

2 Assemble the boxes, taping the pieces in place. For the base, cut strips 1.5cm wide, and stick them inside as this will make the lid fit better.

3 To make your box look like a mobile phone, cut small rectangles of card and glue them onto the lid. For an aerial, stick on a small pencil or a piece cut from a drinking straw.

4 Mix two parts PVA glue with one part water and brush over the box and lid. Cover with four layers of kitchen paper and leave it to dry.

PVA

PVA

CAN'T GET A REAL MOBILE PHONE YET? WELL, FAKE IT! NOT ONLY DOES IT LOOK LIKE A MOBILE, IT'S A SECRET HIDE AWAY TOO!

USE YOUR MOBILE PHONE BOX TO HIDE POCKET MONEY OR ANY SECRET STUFF!

5 Paint your mobile phone. Paint on numbers or symbols or add them with a marker pen when the paint is dry.

VEG OUT

YOU MAY NOT LIKE EATING THEM BUT THEY ARE GREAT FUN TO MAKE! FAKE SOME VEG BY FOLLOWING THE EASY STEPS BELOW! - THEN YOU CAN HAVE FUN PLAYING SHOPS, DECORATING THE KITCHEN OR USING THEM IN SCHOOL PLAYS!

1 To make basic vegetable shapes, crumple newspaper into balls and bind with sticky tape. You can make peppers, cucumbers, potatoes, carrots, tomatoes or anything!

2 For a pepper, roll newspaper tightly into short sausages and tape all round a fatter sausage shape. Add a stork.

3 For a cucumber, snip both ends of a cardboard tube and tape one end down. Stuff the other end with newspaper, then tape it down with sticky tape.

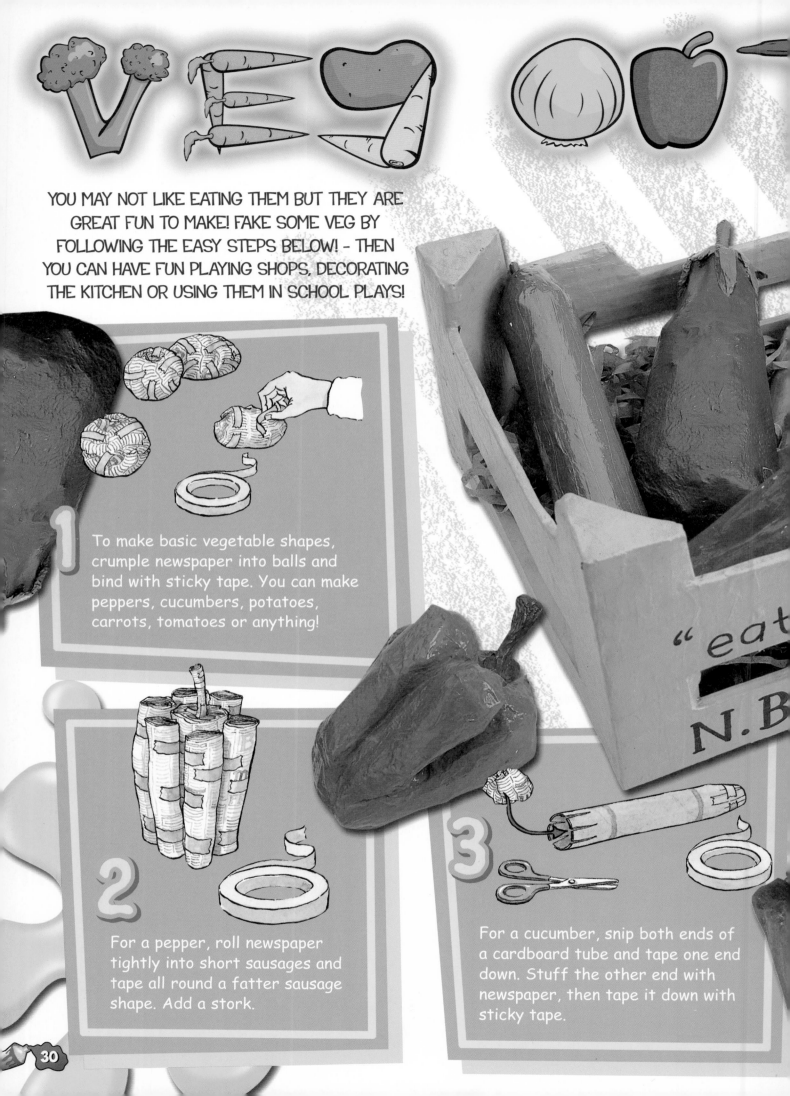

"more vegetables!"

HANAN VEG Cº.

5

For a carrot, roll a rectangle of corrugated card into a cone shape and stick down. Stuff the cone with newspaper to make it firm.

4

Cover all the shapes with four layers of papier maché. Leave them to dry until they're rock hard.

6

Meanwhile, make the crate. Cut the base from a cardboard box leaving about 8cm on each side.

7

From the bit you have just cut off, cut a section 5cm wide to form the top part of the crate.

8

From any remaining card, cut four strips, measuring 15cm x 6cm. Score along the strips at 2cm, 2.8cm and 2cm widths and bend to form triangular sections.

15cm

2cm
2.8cm
2cm

5cm

5cm

9

Stick the crate together following this picture as a guide. Attach the base and the upper section using the four triangular supports. Use plenty of sticky tape.

10

Cover with two layers of papier maché and leave it to dry. Paint your crate brown. Use a sponge to add a wood effect with lighter brown paint. Paint the vegetables and cover with a layer of PVA to make them glossy!

SCARY SKETCH!

THIS CARTOON FACE OF FRANKENSTEIN'S MONSTER LOOKS EXTRA SCARY WITH SCARS, WARTS, PLASTERS AND STITCHES. WHY DON'T YOU ADD YOUR OWN MIXTURE OF HORRID MARKS TO THE FACE BELOW AND CREATE YOUR OWN MONSTER?

Get REWARDED!

DONE YOUR HOMEWORK, CLEANED YOUR BEDROOM, DID THE WASHING UP - DESERVE A REWARD?
MAKE YOURSELF THIS SET OF REWARD CARDS AND EARN YOURSELF A TREAT OR TWO!

M U M BANK

1234 5678 1234 5678

On presentation of this card the **MOTHER** of the undersigned

SIGNED :-

will open her purse and say, **'HELP YOURSELF!'**

Reward Card

5678 1234 5678

ASK AN ADULT TO INITIAL A POINT BOX (SEE ABOVE) IF YOU HAVE BEEN ESPECIALLY WELL BEHAVED. COLLECT 8 POINTS TO RECEIVE THE REWARD AGREED BELOW

THE REWARD IS :-

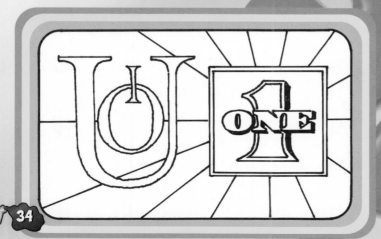

U O U ONE 1

1. FLASH CARD IF SOMEONE IS KIND TO YOU.

2. PROMISE TO RETURN THEIR ACT OF KINDNESS.

signed :

1 Here are 6 reward cards - front & back. Photocopy the pages and then colour them in.

2 Cut them all out and stick the two halves back to back with some card in between to make them firmer. Sign your name or get your parents to sign where appropriate!

3 Cover them with sticky backed plastic. This means that you can rub off any felt tip and use the cards over and over!

On presentation of this card the MOTHER of the undersigned
SIGNED :- Mumllo
will open her purse and say, 'HELP YOURSELF!'

DAD INTERNATIONAL BANK

On presentation of this card the FATHER of the undersigned
Signed :-
will open his wallet or empty his pockets and say, 'HELP YOURSELF!'

Tidy Room Gold card

To earn your pocket money : collect a tick from your parents for each day you keep your room tidy.

Sun Mon Tues Wed Thu Fri Sat
☐ ☐ ☐ ☐ ☐ ☐ ☐

THANX BANK

To say 'Thank you' to your parent(s) invite them to write an 'X' in the box of their choice.

your name :- | ... will help with one activity below.

☐ hoovering/dusting   ☐ shopping
or (write other below)
☐ washing dishes   ☐
☐ weekend break-fast in bed   ☐

35

FOLLOW THE EASY STEPS TO DRAW
SOME CUTE LITTLE WOODLAND CREATURES!

1

Start by drawing an oblong body and round head.

2

The dotted lines help determine which way he will face.

3

Using the dotted lines as a guide, draw on a nose and eyes.

4

Now add cheeks and some arms with paws.

5

Draw some long ears and rub out the dotted lines.

6

Finally add some feet, a tail and colour him in.

1

Draw an oblong body with a smaller round head.

2

Draw a smaller circle for the snout and an oval for the thigh.

3

Add small ears, a foot and an arm.

4

Draw the other arm and foot behind.

5

Now add eyes, a little nose and a big bushy tail.

6

Finally draw some teeth and colour him in.

1

Draw two ovals, making the body one bigger.

2

Add another oval for a thigh and draw an eye and a snout shape.

3

Draw an ear and some front thighs.

4

Now add the legs and rub away any pencil lines you don't want to see.

5

Add details to the feet and ears and draw a long tail.

6

Finally colour him in.

1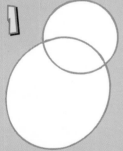

Draw two circles - the body is quite plump.

2

See how the dotted lines give the owl direction. Add ears, legs and feet.

3

Now you can draw the owl some eyes and a beak.

4

Add eyebrows, shape the cheeks and add feathers.

5

The wings are large triangle shapes. Draw a smaller one for the tail.

6

Curve the wings off and make them look feathery, then colour him in.

SCRATCH PICTURES!

ALL YOU NEED IS SOME CARD, SOME COLOURED CRAYONS, A BLACK CRAYON OR PASTEL AND SOMETHING TO SCRATCH WITH, LIKE A DEAD MATCHSTICK.

YOU CAN CREATE ANY PICTURE YOU LIKE. COPY MINE OR DO ONE OF YOUR OWN – IT'S UP TO YOU!

FOLLOW THESE EASY STEPS TO HAVE A SUPER SCRATCH ATTACK...

REMEMBER TO COVER THE SURFACES WHERE YOU ARE WORKING AS IT CAN GET MESSY! FANTASTIC!

1 Use wax crayons or pastels to cover a piece of card in a random pattern of colour. Use as many colours as you like - the brighter the better!

2 Using a black crayon or pastel, colour over the whole piece of card, covering up the colours underneath.

3 Now using a pen nib, dead matchstick or similar pointed object, scratch a picture revealing the colours underneath.

MOVING MUSIC!

HAVE A TRUCK LOAD OF LAUGHS WITH THIS SMASHING ART ATTACK! MAKE A CD RACK THAT YOU CAN MOVE AROUND! IT EVEN DOUBLES UP AS A GREAT TOY FOR A YOUNGER BROTHER OR SISTER!

YOU WILL NEED:

Shoe box, 2 smaller boxes, PVA glue, sticky tape, scrap card, thin straws, plastic bottle tops, newspaper, paint.

1 Get a shoe box. (Make sure CDs fit inside with a bit of space all around.) Make the box stronger by gluing card cut to size on the sides and the base.

2 Find a second box the same width and stick it to the front securely with sticky tape. Then stick a third, smaller box on the front.

3 Stick a smaller curved piece of card of card to the front to form a radiator. Attach a semi-circle of card to the front of that. Then stick on thin straws to make a grill.

4 Make wheel arches from strips of card. Bend them a little and stick them to the side of the third box with sticky tape. Stick plastic bottle caps to the top of each wheel arch for headlights.

5 Turn the truck upside down. On the underneath, stick two strips of corrugated card, the same length as the width of the lorry and about 7cm wide - these are for the wheel axles to go through.

6 Cover the whole lorry with three layers of torn newspaper and diluted PVA glue and water (mixed half and half). Leave it to dry and then paint it. Paint windows and some writing on the side. Add extra details like front and back bumpers made from strips of card.

7 To make wheels, take four cardboard rings (like those found inside sticky tape rolls.) Draw around the rings onto thick card, cut out and attach to both sides of each wheel with sticky tape.

8 Get two sticks, slightly longer than the width of the lorry. Make a hole in one side of a wheel and poke the stick through. Stick in place. Thread a bead on. Push the axle through one of the carriers under the lorry, thread another bead on and finish by attaching the other wheel. Do this to the other wheels as well.

9 Cover the underside of the truck with one layer of torn newspaper and PVA glue mixture. When it's dry, paint the underneath and the wheels. Finally, attach a piece of string to the front of the truck so that you can pull it along.

FOLD-OUT FUTURE!

Follow the simple steps below to create your fortune telling Art Attack! Start by photocopying the page onto white paper, and colouring it in.

flip over

write your 8 predictions

flip over

You will be a champion Sumo wrestler ☆ Soon you will be abducted by aliens ☆

You will be totally bald!

You will be a famous popstar ☆ You will be a fashion super model ☆

You'll be a romantic movie star ☆ You will be goofy with pimples ☆ You'll be gorgeous! ☆

You will be a famous footballer ☆ You will have 14 children, two goldfish and a tatty cat!

THE BIG PICTURE!

1 Take a shoe box. From scrap card, cut strips slightly wider but the same length as the two sides and one short side. Cut zig zags along each strip for teeth and glue to the lid.

2 Scrunch up two balls of newspaper and stick to one end for eyes. Scrunch up two more balls and stick to the other end for nostrils.

PVA

3 Using a mixture of PVA glue mixed in equal parts with water, cover the whole thing with three layers of torn newspaper.

4 When your croc is dry, paint him green. When the paint dries add details like eyes, black nostrils and white teeth.

TRANSFORM AN OLD SHOE BOX INTO A SNAPPY STORAGE BOX! USE IT TO KEEP ALL SORTS OF THINGS IN OR MAKE TWO TO USE AS BOOKENDS WHERE YOU CAN HIDE SECRET THINGS!

SHOE BOXES [AR]E BRILLIANT FOR HAVING [ART] ATTACKS! USE THEM BY [THE]MSELVES OR STICK LOTS [TO]GETHER! YOU CAN MAKE [SH]ELVES, STORAGE BOXES OR MODELS!

YOU WILL NEED:

Scrap card, shoe box, newspaper, paints, PVA glue, sticky tape

PINBALL WIZ

MAKE YOUR VERY OWN PINBALL GAME TO PLAY WITH YOUR FRIENDS!

1

The best kind of box to use is a fruit box as it's quite shallow. Cut a piece of card from a second box to fit inside. (You can always make your own box.)

2

Place a cardboard tube on the flat piece of card, and draw around it. Draw as many of these circles as you like - they will be the pots for your pinball game. Use different size tubes, large and small. Carefully cut out the holes.

ARD!

YOU WILL NEED!

Cardboard boxes, 5 toilet roll tubes, 3 kitchen foil tubes, PVA glue, sticky tape, acrylic paints, marbles, newspapers.

PLAYER 2

100

PLAYER 4

3 Cut the cardboard tubes into equal lengths, each about 3cm long.
Tape one under each hole making sure they are level with the cardboard.

150

200

100

4 Carefully cut a v-shaped notch in the front of the box. Now put the card with the tubes inside the box and tape in place.

5 Cover the whole thing with three layers of papier maché. Leave it to dry until it's rock hard. (Leave the tubes open.)

6 Meanwhile draw a background onto a piece of cardboard box and paint it. Copy this design if you like.

7 When the papier maché is dry, paint the box in bright colours. I added star shapes around the holes. Paint another cardboard tube to match.

8 Stick your picture to the back of the box and then add some numbers to each pot so you can count your score.

HOW TO PLAY!

To play, simply roll a marble down the tube and aim towards the holes. After 3 goes the winner is the one with the highest score!

WAX ON!

WAX AND WATER DON'T MIX. WAX IS GREASY SO THE PAINT JUST SLIDES OFF. THIS GIVES YOU AN OPPORTUNITY TO HAVE SOME WONDERFUL WAXY ART ATTACKS!

Send a secret message. Write on white paper with a candle or a white wax crayon - your friend can paint over the paper to reveal the message!

meet me at 1:30!

Draw simple designs with wax crayons or a candle, then brush with watery paint to create an interesting effect.

You can make fantastic gift wrap or cool posters for your bedroom if you try the effect over large pieces of thin paper.

DON'T FORGET TO COVER ALL YOUR WORK SURFACES - YOU DON'T WANT TO GET WAX OR PAINT ON THE FURNITURE.

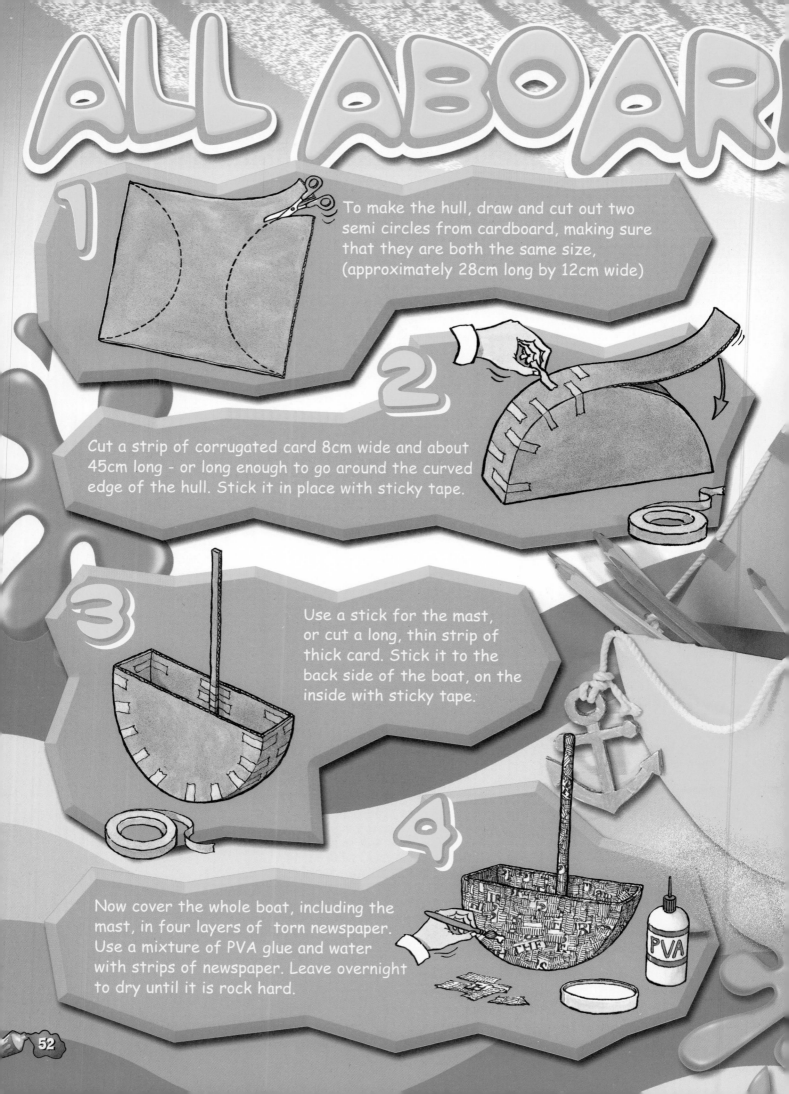

ALL ABOARD!

1 To make the hull, draw and cut out two semi circles from cardboard, making sure that they are both the same size, (approximately 28cm long by 12cm wide)

2 Cut a strip of corrugated card 8cm wide and about 45cm long - or long enough to go around the curved edge of the hull. Stick it in place with sticky tape.

3 Use a stick for the mast, or cut a long, thin strip of thick card. Stick it to the back side of the boat, on the inside with sticky tape.

4 Now cover the whole boat, including the mast, in four layers of torn newspaper. Use a mixture of PVA glue and water with strips of newspaper. Leave overnight to dry until it is rock hard.

SAIL AWAY WITH ANOTHER GREAT ART ATTACK. YOU CAN STICK IT ON THE WALL TO MAKE A SECRET HIDEAWAY OR USE IT AS A DESKTOP TIDY!

YOU WILL NEED:
Card, newspaper kitchen roll, pins PVA glue, paints sticky tape, string, coloured paper.

5 Make a lifebelt by cutting out a ring of card and cutting out the middle. Trace the anchor shape and cut it out. Cover the lifebelt and anchor with two layers of papier maché, using kitchen roll. Leave them to dry.

6 Paint the boat. Attach a long piece of string to the boat with drawing pins or tape. Tie the anchor and lifebelt on. Finally tape some paper sails on made from coloured paper.

TRACE OR COPY THE ANCHOR SHAPE.

53

OUT OF THIS WORLD!

Have an alien attack! Use your felt tip pens to bring this space scene to life!

FOLD OVER FUN!

THESE BARMY BOOKS ARE GREAT! TURN OVER THE PAGE TO FIND THE PICTURES AND THEN FOLLOW THE INSTRUCTIONS BELOW!

I'm so butch

Me

GOA

Complete Idiots Cookery Guide

WHAT ABOUT STICKING FACES OF FRIENDS AND FAMILY ON THE TOP FLAPS USING PHOTOS? THAT'LL MAKE IT EVEN FUNNIER!

1 Photocopy pages 56 and 57 and colour all the cartoon characters in with pens or pencils.

2 Cut the pictures out around the yellow dotted lines and glue them back to back with some paper glue so that all the figures are the same way up.

3 Now carefully cut down all the black dotted lines so that you have flaps.

4 By folding in different flaps you can create some hilarious jumbled up characters on either side!

55

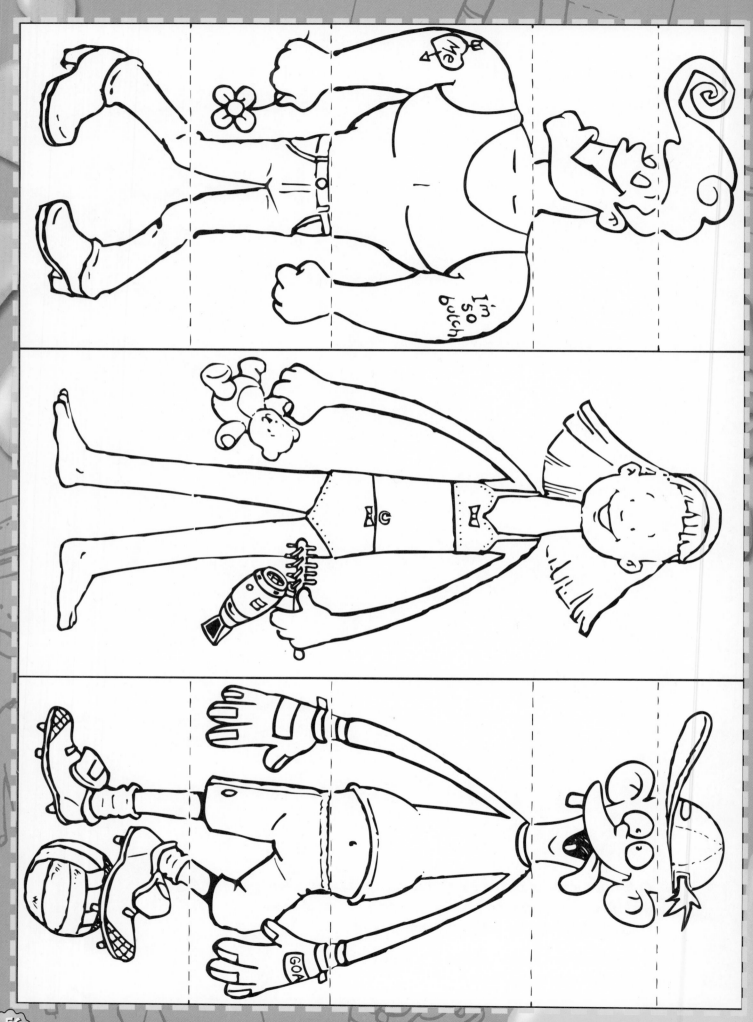

FUN FACE!

This fun face makes a brilliant game or a super storage box. You can throw rolled up balls of paper through the mouth to score points or leave it on your bedside table for storing your bits'n'bobs! All you need is a small box, some card, some newspaper, PVA glue and sticky tape!

1 Place the longer side of a box against some card and draw around it. Then using this rectangle as the shoulders, draw a big face with a really big mouth.

2 Cut out the face and shoulders you have drawn, make sure you remember to cut out the mouth. Stick it to the side of the box, using plenty of sticky tape.

3 To give it a 3D effect, pad out certain areas with crumpled newspaper and kitchen roll - like the lips, nose and t-shirt! Next, stick on rectangles of cardboard for teeth.

4 Finally, paint the whole thing choosing colours that you want. Leave it to dry before you start your game! Scrunch up small balls of paper to throw though the mouth and then fire away!

PVA

59

1 Draw a boy and dog shape onto thick card. Copy the pictures to help you draw the outlines. Cut these shapes out.

2 Crumple up small pieces of tissue paper, kitchen roll or newspaper and stick in place to build up the shapes.

3 Cover the shapes with three layers of papier maché. Leave them to dry.

PVA

4 Now paint. When they're dry, tie some string around the boy's hand and the dog's head.

When you're finished, brush on some PVA glue to make them shine!

TIN BIN

1 For the base and the lid cut circles of thick card 33cm in diameter. Cut a rectangle of corrugated card 54cm wide and 102cm long. Make sure the ridges run length ways so you can bend it round. Also cut two strips of corrugated card 4.5cm wide and 102cm long.

2 Assemble the can by taping the base to the rectangle, wrapping the rectangle around to form a cylinder. Tape the overlapping edges together. Then stick on the two strips, top and bottom, to reinforce your model.

3 Cover the lid, the inside and the outside of the can with four layers of newspaper and diluted PVA glue and leave it to dry.

4 Attach the lid with a hinge made out of sticky tape and thick glue. When that has dried, paint the whole thing like a can.

PVA

TINZ
ART ATTAC
IN HERE
PLEEZ
RECYCLE THE

BE ENVIRONMENTALLY FRIENDLY AND RECYCLE ALL YOUR CANS IN THIS TERRIFIC TIN BIN!

BRIGHT IDEAS!

Make sure you put a plastic bag in your tin bin first so you can empty it easily and take your cans down to the recycling centre!

TINZ

ART ATTACK

IN HERE PLEEZ

RECYCLE THEM!

CLASSIC cola

TRACE iT!

Get into the swing of things with some jungle mania! Simply trace the pictures below onto the right-hand panel, colour and complete for an animal-tastic Art Attack!

ART TOW

THIS IS WHERE I KEEP MY ART STUFF - IF YOU WOULD LIKE AN ART ATTACK ART TOWER, JUST FOLLOW THE STEPS BELOW!

1 Stick down the top of your cereal boxes and cut off one long side of each packet. Then stick all three cereal boxes together to form the bottom three shelves.

2 At the front, glue two large empty matchboxes on the left hand side and a small cereal box on the right. Then glue a small cereal box on top of the matchboxes on the left and two more large matchboxes on top of the small cereal packet. This will form two little shelves and four small drawers.

3 Attach a piece of cardboard to the back of the cereal boxes. Stick 2 toilet roll tubes at the back on the right hand side and stick on a small crisp tin on the other side.

4 Remove the drawers from the matchboxes and cover the whole thing with a mixture of PVA glue and water mixed in equal parts and three layers of torn newspaper strips. Leave this to dry.

...ER!

YOU WILL NEED:

3 cereal boxes, 2 small cereal boxes, sticky tape, scrap card, large empty matchboxes, toilet roll tubes, small crisp tin, newspaper, PVA glue, sticky tape, paints.

wax crayon

67

5 Make some 3D splats by drawing a splat onto cardboard and cutting out. Build it up by sticking on scrunched up paper. Make lots of these, attach them to your art tower and then cover the whole thing with another layer of papier maché.

6 If you would like to add a picture of Neil or any other picture from a magazine, draw around it onto card. Cut out the card shape, cover it with two layers of papier maché and fix it to the back panel. Don't stick your picture on yet.

7 Paint the whole thing white. When that's dry, paint all the splats in bright colours and glue the picture of Neil on. When that's dried, cover the art tower with two coats of PVA glue to give it a shiny finish.

8 Finally, paint the drawers different colours. When they're dry, make two holes in the fronts and thread string through, knotting each end to keep them in place. Now put the drawers back in the matchboxes.

PVA

PVA

On The Buses!

ALL YOU NEED TO CREATE THIS BRILLIANT BUS IS A PAIR OF SCISSORS, SOME COLOURED PENS AND SOME GLUE.

(1) Trace or photocopy the pages overleaf onto white paper.

(2) Stick the pages onto thin card and carefully cut around edge of the bus.

(3) Colour the Art Attack bus in brightly coloured felt tip pens.

(4) Now fold along all the dotted lines and bend the sides down followed by the front and the back.

(5) Stick the sides down using the tabs and some paper glue.

SO TURN OVER AND LET'S GO....
ALL ABOARD THE ART ATTACK BUS!

HOW ABOUT
PHOTOCOPYING THE
BUS SEVERAL TIMES
AND MAKING LOTS
OF THEM?

YOU CAN USE THE SAME BASIC IDEA TO MAKE OTHER VEHICLES. CREATE CARS, TRUCKS OR ANYTHING BY DRAWING THEM IN THE SAME WAY. TRY TO KEEP THE OPPOSITE SIDES IDENTICAL SO THAT THEY WILL MATCH UP WHEN YOU COME TO STICK THEM TOGETHER.

ARK ATTACK!

HERE ARE SOME BOOKENDS WITH A DIFFERENCE - THEY HAVE A MIDDLE TOO! SO FOLLOW THE STEPS TO SAIL AWAY WITH NEIL'S ARK AND CHEER UP ANY BORING BOOKSHELVES!

1

Create the middle section by making a box shape from pieces of card. For the cabin, make a second box, the same width as the first but slightly smaller from front to back. Stick it on top of the larger one. Make the roof from two rectangles of card, and the sides of the roof from two triangles.

2

Lay the middle section on a sheet of cardboard box card and draw around it with a pencil like this. Cut two pieces this shape.

3

Make the bow and stern from long strips of corrugated cardboard the same width as the lower middle section. Tape these in place to the shapes you have just cut out.

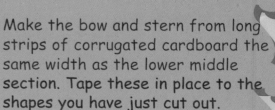

101 THINGS TO MAKE — DEAN

The BIG BOOK of FACTS, RECORDS and LISTS — Elizabeth Holt — Piccolo

SECRET PLACES IN HISTORY — Elizabeth Newbery

TOILETS IN HISTORY — Elizabeth Newbery

HAUNTED HOUSES IN HISTORY — Elizabeth Newbery

DEAD AND BURIED IN HISTORY — Black

DO YOU BELIEVE IN GHOSTS? — John G. Sutton — ELEMENT

Point Non-Fiction — SERIOUSLY WEIRD TRUE STORIES — Herbie Brennan — Black

Point Non-Fiction — SERIOUSLY WEIRD TRUE STORIES 2 — Herbie Brennan

The Seriously Funny guide to the movies — John Byrne — mammoth

4 Stand these on a sheet of cardboard, draw around the bottom and cut out four pieces for the base and deck - then tape these in place too.

5 Add animal shapes cut from cardboard and padded out with kitchen paper. Add a giraffe to the roof and a pig coming out of a window. Just make the head and neck shapes, pad them out and attach them with sticky tape. (See over the page.)

73

6 Cover all the sections with four layers of papier maché. Pay particular attention to the joins and where the animals are joined on to the ark. Leave the whole thing to dry thoroughly for a couple of days.

PVA

7 Have fun painting your bookends in really bright colours! When they're dry add details with a black permanent marker. I even painted some waves along the bottom. Make sure the whole thing is completely dry before putting books in between them.

GIRAFFE LAUGH!

Make a long neck with a couple of narrow pieces of card stuck together and wrapped in kitchen paper. The head is made from two small triangles of cardboard stuck on one end. The ears are smaller triangles of card and the horns are broken matchsticks. Attach the giraffe to the roof with sticky tape and cover with papier maché. Paint the window on afterwards.

PIGGY POWER!

Make a head from a small ball of newspaper. Attach ears made from triangles of card. The snout is a small rolled up piece of paper. Stick the head onto the ark with sticky tape. Then papier maché the whole head and join. The window has been made more three dimensional by sticking on rolled up pieces of paper to make a frame.

GET LABELLED!

Save fuel - Walk to Skool!

SAVE WATER SHOWER POWER

SAVE A TREE RE-CYCLE ME.

Waste Not Want Not

get on your bike

3 R'S RE-USE RE-CYCLE REDUCE

Plant a tree for lonely me

CARRY ME AGAIN!

TURN ME OFF! WHEN YOU GO OUT!

SORT iT! GLASS ALUMINIUM CANS PAPER

PHOTOCOPY, TRACE OR CUT OUT AND COLOUR IN YOUR SUPER COOL RECYCLING LABELS AND STICK THEM WHERE YOU THINK BEST.

Bikes 'r' Best

MAKE A MEAL OF IT!

Mmmmmm!

YOU'LL HAVE LOTS OF MESSY FUN WITH THIS TASTY LOOKING ART ATTACK! BE AS INVENTIVE AS YOU LIKE OR SIMPLY CREATE YOUR FAVOURITE MEAL. JUST MAKE SURE YOU COVER ALL YOUR WORK SURFACES FIRST!

1 Cut a circle from thick card, using a dinner plate as a template.

2 Draw outlines of your favourite food on the cardboard plate. Brush with diluted PVA glue, then stick on cotton wool.

3 Tear coloured tissue paper into large pieces and lay on top of the cotton wool and press down using the tip of your paintbrush. For a neat finish, also cover the edges of the cardboard plate with a few layers of tissue.

4 Leave your plate of food to dry. This will take a few hours - or overnight. Then use some paints to add detail to the food, and to paint the plate.

You will need:

Cardboard
Coloured tissue paper
Cotton wool
PVA glue
Paintbrushes
Paints

Mmmmm!

FAKE FOOD IS GREAT TO USE AS A PROP IN SCHOOL PLAYS, OR JUST TO MAKE FOR FUN!

HOT TIPS!

I'VE MADE A DELICIOUS BREAKFAST, BUT YOU COULD MAKE YOUR FAVOURITE MEAL, LIKE DELICIOUS CHICKEN DRUMSTICKS WITH POTATOES, VEGETABLES AND GRAVY. YOU COULD ALSO CHANGE THE SHAPE OF THE PLATE.

IF YOU HAVEN'T GOT LOTS OF COLOURED TISSUE PAPER, YOU CAN USE NEWSPAPER AND JUST PAINT IT WHITE BEFORE YOU START PAINTING.

WHAT ABOUT MAKING A 3 COURSE DINNER WITH A STARTER AND A DESSERT? JUST MAKE THE PLATES DIFFERENT SIZES.

Picture Parts

START BY CUTTING OUT SEVERAL BOLD, BRIGHT PICTURES FROM CATALOGUES OR OLD MAGAZINES. MAKE SURE THAT THEY ARE FAIRLY SIMPLE.

Take the first picture and cut it in half, horizontally or vertically. Stick it on to a sheet of paper and fill in the missing half with your own drawing, using paints, pens or crayons. A combination of pencil and coloured pencils looks great!

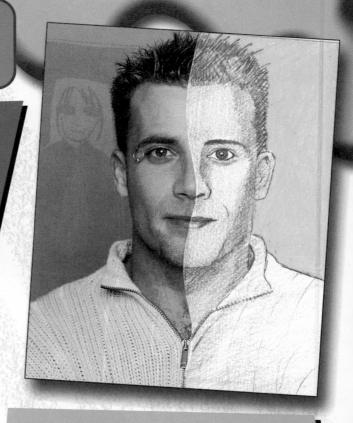

Cut another picture into quarters and stick them in place on to a piece of paper. Fill in the gaps with your own drawing. Use pencil for a striking result!

Cut a third picture into strips and stick them down on to a piece of paper keeping them in the correct position. Use your cartooning skills to fill in the gaps. You can always add things of your own too!

meeee-ow!

Fashion Fun!

WHAT WOULD YOU WEAR IF YOU WERE A POP STAR? YOU CAN CHOOSE ALL SORTS OF COOL OUTFITS OVER THE PAGE AND MAKE YOUR DREAMS COME TRUE!

What to do:

OVER THE PAGE, YOU'LL FIND THE POPSTARS AND ALL THEIR CLOTHES AND ACCESSORIES. PHOTOCOPY THE PAGES AND STICK THEM ONTO THIN CARD. COLOUR EVERYTHING IN AND THEN CUT THEM OUT. ATTACH THE OUTFITS USING THE LITTLE TABS.

IF YOU WANT TO COLOUR THE OUTFITS IN DIFFERENTLY, JUST PHOTOCOPY THEM SEVERAL TIMES AND MAKE SOME MORE!

79

Stick the dolls on to thicker card to make them stronger. To make them stand up snip down the dotted lines and slot the two pieces together.

Have a go at making your own dress up stars! Design lots of outfits for them to wear on different occasions such as The Brit Awards or a film premiere!

LEGGY L[

1 Make a ring of corrugated cardboard about 12cm in diameter. Stuff with crumpled newspaper. Roll up a sheet of newspaper into a sausage and wrap it round. Fasten with sticky tape.

2 Make eight newspaper sausages - one for each leg. Tape in place with plenty of sticky tape. Curl each one up slightly at the end.

3 Cover the whole thing with plenty of diluted PVA and torn strips of newspaper. (About four layers.) Leave it to dry overnight.

UGHS!

TO PLAY THE GAME, THROW RINGS AT THE OCTOPUS, TRYING TO MAKE THEM LAND ON IT'S FEET. USE PLASTIC BRACELETS OR CARDBOARD RINGS FROM THE MIDDLE OF STICKY TAPE.

4 When it's dry, paint in bright colours using poster or acrylic paints. When that's dry you can play hoopla!

83

WHAT A STAR!

SEE HOW YOU SHAPE UP WITH THIS TRICKY ONE - IT WILL CERTAINLY KEEP YOU BUSY FOR A WHILE!

IF YOU WANT
HANG THEM UP,
MAKE A HOLE, PUS
COTTON THROUGH
STICK IT IN PLAC
A DAB OF GLU

1 Tear out or photocopy the opposite page and stick it onto paper. If you want a coloured star, you can either colour the whole thing in or photocopy it onto coloured paper.

2 Now carefully cut around the pattern. Make folds wherever there are dotted lines and cut along the lines where marked.

3 Start sticking it together by matching up the numbers and gluing it using the tabs. Take your time as it can be a bit tricky. If you go wrong just pull the tabs apart and re-glue them.

84

YOUR FINISHED STAR WILL LOOK LIKE THIS 3 DIMENSIONAL ONE!

IF YOU WANT TO MAKE MORE THAN ONE - DON'T FORGET TO PHOTOCOPY IT!

85

IT'S A DOG

THERE'S NOTHING EXCITING ABOUT A TIN OF FOOD
...OR IS THERE? OF COURSE THERE IS - CHEER THE
KITCHEN UP WITH THIS TERRIFIC DOGGY TIN HOLDER!

1 Using these templates cut the shapes out from thick cardboard. Cut out a base measuring at least 8cm square. Make sure that the corrugated ridges in the card run upwards.

YOU WILL NEED:
Cardboard, newspaper, PVA glue, scissors, sticky tape, paints.

HEAD TEMPLATE

TRACE OFF THE BODY TEMPLATE ON TO CARDBOARD. MAKE SURE THE CORRUGATED COLUMNS RUN LENGTHWAYS SO THAT IT BENDS.

2 Bend the body shape around and tape the feet together with sticky tape. Tape this to the base. Use lots of sticky tape to make it really secure.

3 Scrunch up a ball of newspaper and tape it to the bottom of the face to form the snout. Then tape the head to the neck. Use lots of sticky tape to support the head.

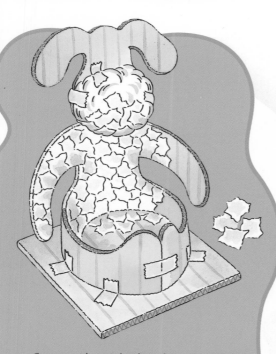

4 Cover the whole thing with three layers of torn newspaper pasted on with PVA glue. Use kitchen roll to build up the shape of the face. Take particular care to cover the neck well.

5 When it has dried, you can decorate it. You could paint him black and white like I have done or any colour you like! Make the base nice and bright.

BOOK PLATES

Photocopy these brilliant book plates onto paper, colour and stick into your favourite books!

This book belongs to...

(name)

THIS BOOK BELONGS TO...

A book from ...

............'s Library

LONG 2

Finger Pup

FOLLOW THE YELLOW BRICK ROAD TO OZ WITH DOROTHY AND HER FRIENDS. TELL YOUR OWN STORY WITH THESE FAB FINGER PUPPETS!

1 Start by photocopying all the finger puppets onto white paper.

2 Stick it on to cereal box card with paper glue to make your puppets stronger.

3 Carefully cut all of them out following the dotted lines. Be extra careful when cutting the finger holes out. (Ask an adult to help you if it's a bit fiddly.)

4 Now pop them on your fingers and away you go!

You could even draw and paint your own backgrounds on paper. Stick the backgrounds into a large box and carefully cut holes in the back for your hands.

HOW ABOUT PAINTING YOUR
FINGERS WITH FACE PAINTS
AND PAINTING VARNISH ON
YOUR NAILS FOR A FEW
LEGGY LAUGHS?

WIZ

Paint Pot Tidies!

1 Cut a rectangle of corrugated cardboard and roll it up to make a cylinder. Make sure the ridges run vertically. You can make it any size that you like - it depends on what you want to use it for.

2 Stand the cylinder on a sheet of cardboard and draw around it. Cut out this circle and stick it in place, to form the base.

WHY NOT MAK SMALLER ONE PENCILS OR A R BIG ONE FOR RUBBISH BI

3 Cover the paint pot, inside and out, with four layers of papier maché (diluted PVA glue and torn newspaper strips). Leave it to dry until it's rock hard.

PVA

5 Punch holes either side near the top of the pot. Cut a strip of card and paint it silver. Punch a hole at either end and attach it to the pot using paper fasteners.

4 Now comes the fun bit! Paint your pot, including the label. Then paint the drips all around the top. Use lots of thick paint to make it look really realistic.

Eyes are a great way of adding character to a face.
Look at these great tips to help you master drawing all sorts of eyes!

Start by copying these eyes, they show the basic shape of most eyes, including the irises, pupils, eye rims and eyebrows. Eyes are not symmetrical so don't worry if they don't look identical.

Men's

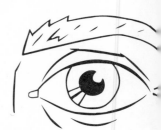

Men's eyes may not be as soft as women's eyes. The eyebrows can be bushier and they have more definite lines around them.

Lady's

Women's eyes may be smaller and more delicate. The eyebrows are often straighter and usually not so bushy. Make eyelashes thicker and more shaped for very feminine eyes.

Angry

Angry eyes look as thought they are screwed up. The eyebrows slant downwards towards the top of the nose. The eyes become narrower and slant downwards too. The lines around the eyes are more angled and there are more of them than normal. The top of the nose may crease.

Smiling

Happy eyes need to twinkle. The eyes form a banana shape. There are laughter lines around the eyes where the smiling mouth pulls the side of the face upwards. Small bags may appear under the eyes as the cheeks rise.

Scared

The pupil shrinks with fear and the eyes look huge. The eyebrows rise into the forehead. You can see all of the iris - the coloured bit around the pupil - as the eyes are opened up really wide.

Sleeping

The eyes are closed and relaxed. Draw curved lines with lashes along the bottom. Add lines curved the opposite way to indicate the top of the eyelids. Unless you are drawing an older person, the eye area will probably be quite wrinkle free.

Suspicious

The eyes become narrow as the face forms a frown. Creases appear at the top of the nose. Draw the eyes looking sideways with the pupils and irises on one side to emphasise thought and suspicion.

Crying

The eyes become soft and tears form in the corners. Small creases appear by the outside edge and the eyelids go wobbly. The eyebrows may move downwards and the eyes would become red if in colour.

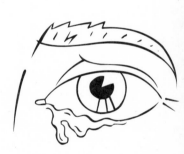

Side View

Draw the outline of the nose and some of the forehead so you can position the eye. Draw an arrowhead shape with a semi circle for the front of the eye. Fill in with a pupil and iris - both semi circles. Add a line to represent lashes. Finally draw an eyebrow over the eye.

Cartoon

Just use your imagination and personal style to draw cartoon eyes. The one I have done is really simple. Draw big ovals with little oval pupils for the eyes. Add slanted lines for lashes. The nose is just straight lines. Easy!

TURN OVER THE PAGE TO HAVE A GO YOURSELF!

Finish the expressions on the faces below by drawing the appropriate eyes.

CRAZY CURLS!

YOU CAN USE PAPER CURLS TO MAKE GREAT TEXTURED PICTURES. TRY MAKING THIS CURLY TREE TOP, OR MAKE UP SOME OF YOUR OWN!

THERE ARE TWO WAYS OF CURLING A STRIP OF PAPER –

1 Roll the paper tightly around a pencil. Pull out the pencil and you will be left with a tightly curled paper coil.

2 Pull the paper across the blade of a pair of scissors or a ruler with your thumb on top of the paper. This will produce a curly paper spiral.

WHAT OTHER PICTURES CAN YOU CREATE? USE CURLY PAPER FOR HAIR, GRASS, COLLAGE EFFECTS, ANYTHING! IT'S VERY EFFECTIVE AND GREAT FUN!

TO MAKE THE CURLY TREE...

1 Cut a tree trunk shape from card or brown paper and stick it onto coloured card. Leave enough room to add your tree top.

2 Curl loads of strips of paper - use two different shades of green for a good effect. You can use coloured paper or colour in plain paper with felt tips.

3 Glue one end of the paper strips to the paper. Carry on until you've made a curly tree top.

Pasta Pictur

YOU DON'T HAVE TO BE A GOOD COOK TO BE GREAT WITH FOOD! WHAT ABOUT HAVING AN ART ATTACK IN THE KITCHEN INSTEAD?

Make sure you ask an adult for anything in the kitchen. I used several different kinds of pasta, you could also use rice, lentils and chick peas.

In fact any dry food can help to make a brilliant Art Attack!

What to do:

Cut a piece of cardboard from a box to make the base for your picture. (It needs to be quite firm as you will probably use a lot of glue.)

Draw the outline of your picture in pencil. Keep the picture simple and think of the pasta shapes as you draw. A house picture is perfect. You can create all sorts of textured effects for the roof, the grass, the pathway, and so on.

Start to stick on your pieces of pasta. Use long pieces for walls, tree trunks and edges, use twirls for fences, shrubs and roofing and use tubes for trees or flowers. You can use whole pieces or broken pieces - it's up to you!

PASTA CAN BE A GREAT WAY TO MAKE PICTURES AND COLLAGES 3 DIMENSIONAL. WHAT ABOUT PAINTING A BACKGROUND AROUND THE PASTA SHAPES?

HERE'S A GREAT WAY TO MAKE A FUNNY BIRTHDAY CARD! STICK A PASTA BOWTIE AND NOSE ON A PHOTO!

YOU CAN PAINT THE PASTA IF YOU WANT. JUST USE ORDINARY POSTER PAINT OR ACRYLIC PAINTS AND LET IT DRY BEFORE YOU PICK IT UP.

POSTER PAINT

99

Trace It!

This one is really cooking! Simply trace the pictures from the left onto the right-hand panel and create some tasty treats!

CRAZY CAULDRON!

Treat yourself this Hallowe'en with a cool cauldron to collect all those goodies!

PVA

1 Blow up a round balloon and cover it with at least eight layers of diluted PVA glue and torn strips of newspaper. Hang it up to dry overnight.

2 Pop the balloon. Trim the shell so that it looks bowl shaped. Cut three pieces of corrugated card about 9cm square. Roll them up and tape to the base of the shell to form legs.

3 Roll up a sheet of newspaper and tape it to the top edge. Cover the whole thing inside and out, with torn strips of black tissue paper. Leave it to dry until it's rock hard.

PVA

YOU DON'T HAVE TO ADD LEGS - WHAT ABOUT JUST PAINTING A FUNNY FACE! FANTASTIC!

4

When dry, paint it all black and then give it an aged look by dabbing a bit of bronze, gold or orange paint over the surface. Make a hole in either side and thread a length of string through to make a handle.

FACE IT!

Face painting takes a bit of practice but it's great fun. You can turn yourself into animals, monsters or even aliens! And what better time than Hallowe'en!

1 Sponge on a base of white on half of your face. Wet the sponge and squeeze it hard. Rub it lightly over the paint and then dab it on your face. Close your eye when sponging over it.

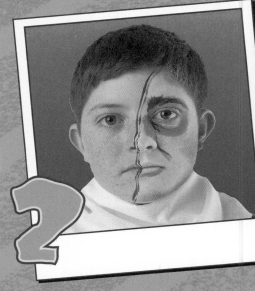

2 Now edge the white paint with a black line. Use grey to create shadows under the eye for a ghoulish look. Add some grey shadows around the nose, jaw and bottom lip.

3 Get your red face paint out to create some nasty blood drips and hideous eye effects! Draw on a scar with black and red paint.

104

WITCH'S CAT

1

Sponge on a base of blue and add white around the mouth. Use a fairly dry sponge to press colour onto the face rather than rubbing it. Avoid the eye area.

2

Using a crayon, brush or finger, sweep some green face paint under and above the eye. (Be careful as this is a delicate area.) Add some white brush strokes around the mouth and eyebrows.

3

Paint a little red tongue below the lip. Add black whiskers, a nose and outline the eyes. Also paint some black dots around the mouth. Purrfect!

TECHNIQUES

BLENDING

Use a damp sponge to merge two or more colours together. This can be tricky with dry colours so work fast or dampen the colours a bit.

OUTLINING

Make certain areas stand out by defining them with a darker colour. You can use a brush or face crayon to add details and outline.

STIPPLING

Use a fairly dry sponge to dab colour onto the skin rather than rubbing. You can create stubble or shadows this way.

MAKE SURE THAT YOU ALWAYS PROTECT YOUR CLOTHING AND THAT YOU USE PROPER FACE PAINTS SUITABLE FOR SKIN. ALSO - ALWAYS GET AN ADULT'S PERMISSION!

Delightful Lantern!

Create a fabulous lantern with the help of some coloured tissue and a torch! It's easy to do and it looks wicked!

1 Start by tracing off the pattern on the opposite page and transferring it to black card. If you don't have black card, another colour will do or just colour plain card in.

2 Now cut up pieces of coloured tissue paper and glue them behind each of the gaps. Use only small amounts of glue. Stick on different coloured tissue paper so you get a nice colourful effect.

3 Copy this pattern until you have four side pieces. Carefully cut out each section so there are lots of gaps and you are left with frames.

4 Fold along the side tabs and glue the four sides together. Then fold in the bottom tabs and stick down. Place a torch with a low wattage bulb in the lantern and watch it light up.

REMEMBER, IT'S NOT SAFE TO USE A BULB WITH A HIGH WATTAGE (OVER 40 OR 60 WATTS) OR A CANDLE AS YOUR LANTERN COULD CATCH FIRE.